READ

A Bible Study Plan for Unpacking God's Word

CYNDEE OWNBEY

ISBN 978-1-7334710-2-2 (Paperback)

What People Are Saying...

"I have found the READ method to be such a helpful way for me to understand Scripture and to be able to apply what I've discovered."

"It got me back into God's Word daily."

"I liked that I was in charge of the information, so to speak. I was able to seek out reputable sources and pull from different areas instead of listening to one person's interpretation of what the passage meant."

"I can take it and apply it to any book of the Bible."

"Absolutely love it. It gives me steps for more clearer understanding. It has become a 'rabbit hole' as I dig deeper, and I love it. I'm learning so much and seeing things so differently."

"Love, love, love the READ study plan."

"I had to think and pray so I could know what God had for me, not what someone else thought."

The law of the Lord is perfect, restoring the soul;
The testimony of the Lord is sure, making wise the simple.
The precepts of the Lord are right, rejoicing the heart;
The commandment of the Lord is pure, enlightening the eyes.
The fear of the Lord is clean, enduring forever;
The judgments of the Lord are true; they are righteous altogether.
They are more desirable than gold, yes, than much fine gold;
Sweeter also than honey and the drippings of the honeycomb.
Moreover, by them Your servant is warned;
In keeping them there is great reward.
Who can discern his errors? Acquit me of hidden faults.
Also keep back Your servant from presumptuous sins;
Let them not rule over me; Then I will be blameless,
And I shall be acquitted of great transgression.
Let the words of my mouth and the meditation of my heart
Be acceptable in Your sight, O Lord, my rock and my Redeemer.

Psalm 19:7-14 (NASB)

Table of Contents

PART 1

An Introduction to READ

Before you dive in...

I am so excited about the journey you are about to embark upon.

God's Word is so rich! There is much He wants us to learn and discover.

If you are new to the READ method or inductive-type Bible study, let me encourage you to stick with it! You may struggle a bit at first as you get accustomed to the format. But, in time, you will find your rhythm and discover the rewards of regularly engaging with God's Word.

TO COMPLETE THIS STUDY, YOU WILL NEED JUST 4 THINGS:

1. **A Bible**—I suggest a word-for-word translation (see the chart on page 26). A study Bible can be helpful, but it is not necessary.

2. **Access to a commentary**—If you have a study Bible, the notes at the bottom are a commentary. You can also find many free online commentaries at biblestudytools.com, biblegateway.com, blueletterbible.org, netbible.org, and studylight.org. Most of these commentary sites also offer a free app you can download onto your phone. You may decide to invest in a printed commentary. You can find a list of my favorite commentaries at womensministrytoolbox.com/read-resources.

3. **Access to another translation of the Bible**—I suggest using a thought-for-thought translation (see the chart on page 26). Selecting a translation from the opposite end of the chart on page 26 will add depth to your study time. Most of the websites mentioned above also offer a variety of translations online and in their apps.

4. **READ Weekly Worksheets**—In order to take time to savor and thoroughly unpack God's Word, I strongly recommend reading only one chapter each week. You will be blessed as you slow down, dig deep, and really digest each chapter of Scripture.

As with any Bible study, the more you put into your study time, the more you'll get out of it! Check out the reading plans for pacing suggestions on pages 39-42 to pace yourself.

It is my deepest and most heartfelt prayer that you will grow in your ability and confidence to study God's Word. I am praying that God will open your eyes so you may see wonderful things in His law (Psalm 119:18 NIV).

Humbly His,

Cyndee Ownbey

Women's Ministry Toolbox

History of READ Bible Study

In the early spring of 2016, our morning Bible study group wrapped up our current session. Without the weekly meetings and accountability of my Bible study group, my time in the Word stalled. Within weeks, God drew my attention to the sorry state of my "quiet" time—really the lack thereof. As I struggled against the promptings of the Holy Spirit, I was forced to acknowledge that I spent more time that spring reading my Bible study book than I did the actual Bible.

My feelings did not line up with what I knew God was asking me to do—to put down the Bible study book and learn to study Scripture on my own without a Bible study author or pastor at my side.

Maybe you've found yourself offering God some of the same excuses I did:

- I'm not smart enough to study Scripture on my own. I don't have a seminary degree.

- I don't know where or how to start. There are 66 books—should I read them in order?

- Just reading my Bible can be so dry and boring at times.

- I don't have hours to spend each day studying the Bible.

Thankfully, God placed several resources in my path, including *Women of the Word* by Jen Wilkin and *Multiply: Disciples Making Disciples* by Francis Chan. As I read through each resource, a clear pattern of studying Scripture emerged – observation, interpretation, and application (OIA). The OIA method was the basis for most of the Bible study plans I encountered.

I somewhat reluctantly worked my way through four books of Scripture using variations of the OIA method. As I worked through each book of the Bible, I refined my process. I held tightly to Acts 4:13 which says, "When they saw the courage of Peter and John and realized that they were unschooled, ordinary men, they were astonished and they took note that these men had been with Jesus" (NIV). Like Peter and John, I didn't have a seminary degree. All I wanted was to meet with Jesus in His Word.

By the end of the summer, I held in my hands the first draft of the READ Bible study worksheet. My heart burned with the desire to share what I had learned with my church Bible study group. I met our Bible study coordinator for lunch, armed with a proposal to teach our Bible study attendees how to study Scripture for themselves using the READ worksheets. I was a nervous wreck and greatly relieved to discover God had planted the desire for a Scripture-based, inductive-type Bible study on the hearts of team members almost two years prior. I was utterly humbled that He was using me to help bring that prayer to fruition.

In the fall of 2016, our small church had 40 women sign up to study 1st and 2nd Timothy using the READ Bible study method. Over the weeks, their confidence, knowledge, and skills grew. Like learning to ride a bike without the training wheels, they were studying God's Word all by themselves!

In the years since, I've shared the READ Bible study method with thousands of women. It's the tool I continue to use during my personal quiet time.

I pray you'll find it just as useful!

Why READ?

The READ Bible study method, like other inductive-type Bible studies, is successful because it encourages familiarity, digestion, connections, examination, application, growth, and understanding.

1. FAMILIARITY - Repetition breeds familiarity and begins the process of memorization. The more we know God's Word, the more we know about God. See Psalm 119:10-11.

2. DIGESTION - Slowing down to spend dedicated time on one passage allows the Holy Spirit to speak and provides time to digest God's Word. See Joshua 1:8.

3. CONNECTIONS – Examining how Scripture connects with other passages leads us to see consistent themes throughout the Bible.

4. EXAMINATION- God doesn't specify how much time we should spend or how quickly we should read His Word. Sometimes we treat it like a race. We learn more by digging deeply than by skimming the surface. Unpacking the cultural and historical context brings Scripture to life by providing insight that can change the way we view and understand Scripture.

5. APPLICATION - It's not enough to study the Word; we must act upon the Word. How we apply God's Word matters. See James 1:22-25.

6. GROWTH & UNDERSTANDING - Studying Scripture gives us a greater understanding of who God is and what He has done for us. When we apply that knowledge to our lives, we reflect His image. See Romans 12:2, Psalm 119:18, Proverbs 2:1-5, and 2 Timothy 3:16-17.

PART 2

How to READ

R stands for Record

On the following pages, you'll find excerpts from the READ Weekly Worksheets which will guide you through the record, explore, apply, and do exercises.

Together we'll look at Joshua 1:1-18. Though it's not an entire chapter, it is long enough for you to get a good feel for the READ Bible study method.

Before we begin, take a moment to pray. You may want to ask the Holy Spirit to renew and transform your mind as you study God's Word. (See John 14:26 and Romans 12:2.)

Your first task each week is to record the answers to the "w" questions below.

The 6 W's

1. Who wrote the passage?

2. To whom was the passage written?

3. When was the passage written?

4. Where was the passage written?

5. What genre was the passage written in? See page 21.

6. Why was this passage written?

I like to record the "w" facts on my READ Weekly Worksheet the first week of Bible study. Then I recall and reflect on them each week after that. Doing so helps me to remember the context of the Scripture passages.

To find the answers to these questions, we need to pull out some Bible study materials.

Open a commentary or study Bible (physically or online) and search for the introduction to the book of Joshua.

Read through the introduction looking for the answers to the "w" questions and record your answers below.

Who?	To whom?
When?	Where?
What genre?	Why?

Were you able to find all of the answers? Sometimes historians aren't certain, don't know, or disagree. Don't worry about any blanks or uncertain answers.

In my research, I found Joshua *may* have written this book. It was written to the Israelites around 1200-1170 BC. The book of Joshua records Joshua's leadership and the fulfillment of the covenant between God and the Israelites. This book falls into the history genre. Scholars aren't sure where the book of Joshua was written. Your findings should be similar.

A NOTE ON GENRES

The Bible is composed of many different literary forms or genres – kind of a compilation of different types of books all put together in one. Scholars divide the books of the Bible into anywhere from 5-10 different genres.

This table divides the Bible into five genres.

1. History – Old Testament history of the Jewish people, New Testament history of the early church and history of Jesus' life

2. Prophecy –Predictions that have been fulfilled and some that have not yet happened

3. Letters – Personal letters to the church

4. Wisdom Poetry – Answers to questions about life and living

5. Law – A picture of God's sovereign will and character

When you record the genre, you're welcome to use the Genres of the Bible chart on the next page or one you've found in your own Bible resources.

Genres of the Bible

HISTORY	PROPHECY	LETTERS	LAW
History of the Jewish people, Jesus, & early church	*Predictions fulfilled & yet to come*	*Personal letters to the church*	*God's will and character*
OLD TESTAMENT	**OLD TESTAMENT**	**NEW TESTAMENT**	**OLD TESTAMENT**
Joshua	Isaiah	Romans	Genesis
Judges	Jeremiah	1 & 2 Corinthians	Exodus
Ruth	Lamentations	Galatians	Leviticus
1 & 2 Samuel	Ezekiel	Ephesians	Numbers
1 & 2 Kings	Daniel	Philippians	Deuteronomy
1 & 2 Chronicles	Hosea	Colossians	
Ezra	Joel	1 & 2 Thessalonians	
Nehemiah	Amos	1 & 2 Timothy	
Esther	Obadiah	Titus	
	Jonah	Hebrews	**WISDOM POETRY**
	Micah	James	*Answers to questions about life & living*
NEW TESTAMENT	Nahum	1 & 2 Peter	
Matthew	Habakkuk	1, 2, & 3 John	**OLD TESTAMENT**
Mark	Zephaniah	Philemon	Job
Luke	Haggai	Jude	Psalms
John	Zechariah		Proverbs
Acts	Malachi		Ecclesiastes
	NEW TESTAMENT		Song of Songs
	Revelation		

Put any study materials away. You just need your Bible and the Holy Spirit for the next part.

Our next step is to record what the passage is about.

What takes place in these verses? Who are the main characters? Create an outline of events if you wish, or just jot down the important information you'd need to explain this passage to another person.

Open to Joshua 1:1-18 and record what the passage says.

I trust you've done a great job!

Before we move on to the next step, **record any repeated and key words in this passage.**

I made a note of these words and phrases: *Moses, dead, land, Jordan, be strong and courageous, servant, commanded,* and *go.* It's okay if your list is different than mine.

Next, we need to record the main idea for the passage.

Your sentence(s) can be any length as long as it communicates the main idea of the passage. You may wish to have one main idea for each section (usually titled in your Bible) of the passage or a main idea for the entire chapter.

You are simply summarizing what has happened in the passage of Scripture or what the author of this passage has said. Take care not to interpret the passage; just record the facts.

I admit, I sometimes make this task harder than it needs to be. I find using the key words, repeated words, and the bold headings in my Bible to be helpful.

Record the main idea (one sentence or one sentence per section) in the box below.

My main sentence for this passage was: After the death of Moses, God installs Joshua as the new leader of the Israelites, which leads Joshua to make preparations to cross the Jordan. Don't overthink what you wrote down – anything longer or shorter is fine, too.

Excellent! We're ready to move from recording to exploring.

E stands for Explore

Let's explore the passage.

Grab another translation of the Bible. If you have one handy, great! If not, they are easily accessible online and through several different apps (see page 11). Select a translation different from the Bible translation you usually read.

A NOTE ON BIBLE TRANSLATIONS

Bible translations allow us to read and study the Bible in our own language.

I am thankful for the diligence and education of biblical scholars. They have taken the original languages of the Bible (Hebrew and Aramaic in the Old Testament and Greek in the New Testament) and made them accessible for people to read in other languages. Painstaking efforts have been made over centuries to ensure that Scripture was accurately copied and translated.

There are three basic types of translations: word-for-word, thought-for-thought, and paraphrase.

1. **Word-for-word Translations:** Allow the Bible reader to know the specific word choice and phrases used by the authors of the Bible. There is approximately one English word or phrase for every word or phrase translated from the original language. When possible, the same word order is kept. More formal, it is often used for in-depth personal study. Some people find it more challenging to read. Examples: Amplified, New American Standard Bible, Christian Standard Bible, and English Standard Version.

2. **Thought-for-thought Translations:** Authors rearrange the order of the words so it makes the most sense to the reader. Whole sentences are examined (thought-for-thought) and re-written, so they are more easily understood. Meaning, not the exact wording, is the focus. Thought-for-thought translations are most often used for everyday reading and group study, and most people find them easier to read. There is a greater risk of mistranslations, and great care must be taken to ensure the true meaning

of the original text remains. Examples: Contemporary English Version, New International Readers Version, and New Living Translation.

3. **Paraphrase:** Readers are given the overall picture of the biblical text. Ideas, not words, are the focus. Often the text takes on a whole new meaning. A paraphrase may use the word flashlight instead of a lamp. Paraphrases are most commonly used for devotional reading. Examples: The Message, The Living Bible, and the Easy-to-Read version.

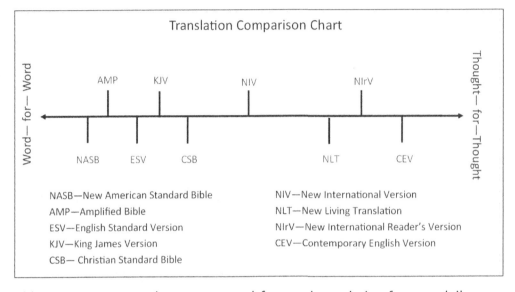

Side note: I recommend you use a word-for-word translation for your daily study time. Then, when exploring another translation, try a thought-for-thought translation or a paraphrase.

Read Joshua 1:1-18 in a different translation.

Make a note of the translation you used and any new things the Holy Spirit has brought to your attention.

While your answers will be specific to the translations you used, I've included a few of my insights as an example. I compared the ESV (English Standard Version) to the CEV (Contemporary English Version).

- In verse 5, the ESV specifies that God said He will not forsake Joshua. That information is omitted in the CEV.

- The CEV uses the "brave," but the ESV uses "courageous."

- Verse 8 in the CEV says, "never stop reading," but the ESV says, "the Book of the Law shall not depart from your mouth."

Sometimes I find I understand parts of the passage better in a different translation.

Let's explore some more by following the cross-references.

CROSS-REFERENCES

Cross-references lead the reader to connecting verses. Uncovering repeated themes, words, events, and people provide a greater understanding of God's Word. Following cross-references can also help us unpack places in the passage that may be confusing as Scripture helps us interpret Scripture.

Cross-references may be listed in the margin, at the bottom of the page, or after the Scripture verse. Look for superscript letters of the alphabet.

As you make a note of other places in Scripture that communicate a similar message, also consider:

- How the passage connects to the passage immediately before and after.

- How the passage fits into the greater story of the Bible (creation – fall – redemption – restoration).

Make a note of how the cross-references you've followed have given you a greater understanding of the passage. If you see a connection between this passage and the greater story of the Bible, make a note of that too.

Were you able to find other places in Scripture that communicated a similar message?

I followed Numbers 27:18-23 and read about Moses commissioning Joshua. In Deuteronomy 11:24-25, I read the original covenant the LORD made with Moses and the people of Israel. I discovered Deuteronomy 31:7-8 and Joshua 10:25 also include the phrase "be strong and courageous." I saw hints of God's plan for restoration as the people of Israel will be restored to the Promised Land.

We've got one more step to take as we explore this Scripture passage.

Up to this point, the Bible and the Holy Spirit have guided our study of the Word. Now it's time to pull back out a Bible commentary.

A NOTE ON COMMENTARIES

Commentaries provide insight and explanation of Bible verses, passages, and books based upon the original language, context, grammar, and historical background. Commentaries may also include illustrations and personal application. Written by biblical scholars and pastors, commentaries often include cultural and historical information that will expand your understanding of the Scripture passage.

Since most of us have not studied the history of biblical times and few of us are familiar with common agricultural or fishing methods of that day, solid resources are key in unpacking the meaning of the passage we are studying. I find almost every time I use a commentary I gain new insight and understanding.

You may wish to ask your pastor which commentaries they recommend, as each author writes through the lens of their theology, which may be different from your church's beliefs.

If you have a study Bible, the notes (usually found at the bottom of the page) are a commentary. Don't forget to refer to the list on page 11 for online commentaries.

Select a commentary and make a note of any information you find interesting or helpful.

I used the Jamieson-Fausset-Brown commentary available on www.biblestudytools.com.

Here are a few things I learned:

- Joshua probably assumed his role immediately after the death of Moses.

- Joshua's original name was Oshea. His new name was Jehoshua or Joshua, meaning "God's salvation."

- Joshua served as Moses' official attendant and would have been well trained to take over.

- Joshua's victory, though certain, was dependent on his firm and inflexible adherence to the Law of God.

You may have found similar or different information, but I hope your commentary pointed out the significance of Joshua's new name.

A is for Apply

You've done a super job digging deeper and exploring the meaning of this passage!

Let's apply what we've learned.

Sometimes we mistakenly look at the Bible as a book about us when in reality, it's a book about God.

Re-read the passage looking for clues about God.

What does this passage tell me about God? What does the text say about God's character or His promises?

Maybe you wrote down:

- God keeps His promises. (verse 3)

- God is always with us. (verse 5)

- God provides for His people. (verse 10)

God's character will be more obvious in some passages than it is in others.

We can also look for personal application in the scripture passages we read.

What does this passage say about God's children? Does the text point out a sin? Does it list a responsibility?

I was drawn to verse 8 and was reminded of our responsibility to know and study God's Word. I also wrote about our responsibility to obey God and our failure (sin) when we don't.

D stands for Do

James 1:22 tells us we are to "be doers of the word and not hearers only."

Let's look at what God is asking you to do in light of the passage you've read. Guided by the Holy Spirit, prayerfully seek God's direction before you answer.

- Is there a habit God wants you to acquire or let go?

- Is God asking you to pray specifically about something or someone?

- Is God prompting you to seek forgiveness or forgive someone?

- Is there something you need to confess to God?

- Is there someone God wants you to encourage?

- Is there someone God wants you to serve?

- Is there an area in which God is prompting you to choose holiness over freedom?

Sometimes it's crystal clear after reading a passage what it is God wants you to do. Other times we may not be certain. Pray and ask God to show you what He wants you to do.

Try to answer as deeply and as honestly as you can.

What does God want you to do today or this week to develop Christ-like character and habits?

Our very last weekly task is to remember.

Almost every week, I sense the Lord drawing my attention to at least one verse. As I study, I also usually discover at least one fact or insight that I don't want to forget. Here is a place to highlight the verses and facts you want to be sure to remember.

What does God want you to remember from this week's study?

I pray your time READing this passage led to fresh discoveries and increased your understanding of God.

Bible Study Lessons in Joshua

Before I send you out on your own to study God's Word with the Holy Spirit as your guide, I want to share a few things I discovered on a deeper dive into Joshua 1:7-8.

Let's look again at verses 7 and 8.

Be strong and very courageous. Be careful to obey all the law my servant Moses gave you; do not turn from it to the right or to the left that you may be successful wherever you go. Keep this Book of the Law always on your lips; meditate on it day and night so that you may be careful to do everything written in it. Then you will be prosperous and successful (NIV).

According to The Wiersbe Bible Commentary, the Book of Law would have contained:

1. Book of the Covenant (God's covenant with the people given to Abraham)

2. Record of the journey from Egypt to Canaan

3. Special regulations for dealing with the inheritance

4. A song Moses taught the people

5. The first five books of the Bible.[1]

Though it's not as lengthy as the Bible we use, it's still a significant amount of text for Joshua to know and understand. God doesn't just tell Joshua *what* he should know. He also tells him *how* he should study the Book of the Law. Looking at verse 8, we see Joshua was supposed to:

1. Keep this book of law always on your lips

2. Meditate on it day and night

---

[1] Wiersbe, W., 2007. The Wiersbe Bible Commentary. Colorado Springs, CO: David C. Cook, p.383.

3. Do everything written in it.

As Wiersbe points out, "Joshua had to take time to read it daily and make it a part of his inner person by meditating on it. The Hebrew word translated "meditate" means "to mutter." It was the practice of the Jews to read Scripture aloud (Acts 8:26-40) and talk about it to themselves and to one another (Deut. 6:6-9)."[2]

The quantity and complexity of the Book of the Law would have required:

    1. Observation - Intensive and intentional study (Record Tasks)

    2. Reflection - Marinate and soak (Explore Tasks)

    3. Application – Practice, apply, do it (Apply and Do Tasks)

    4. Memorization (Do Task)

I believe it's fair to assume that the same instructions God gave Joshua for studying the Book of the Law would benefit us too.

Do you see the connections? Joshua's Bible study method is strikingly similar to the OIA (see page 13) and READ Bible study method. May the strength and courage Joshua received by studying the Book of the Law also be our reward as we study God's Word.

---

[2] Wiersbe, W., 2007. The Wiersbe Bible Commentary. Colorado Springs, CO: David C. Cook, p.383.

READ on Your Own

Now that you've practiced using the READ Bible study method, it's time to dig in!

1. Select a book of the Bible to study.

2. Determine the pace at which you'll proceed. I suggest studying one chapter over a week, devoting about 15 or more minutes each day to work through the READ Weekly Worksheet.

3. Pray, asking God to open your eyes and mind each day before opening God's Word. Consider praying one of the Scripture passages noted in the Prayer Scripture section.

4. Read or re-read the Scripture passage each day.

5. Complete at least one section of the worksheet. See the Suggested Reading Plan on the next pages for pacing and section suggestions.

6. Pray, thanking God for any fresh insight you received during your time in the Word.

Savor the slower pace of studying God's Word. You'll find your retention and knowledge greatly increase when the Scriptures are allowed to marinate in your mind.

Suggested READing Plans

EVERY DAY
• Start with prayer – ask God to open your eyes as you read His Word. • Read or re-read the chapter for the week. • Complete the daily activity listed below. • Close with prayer – thank God for any fresh insight you gained from your time in the Word.

THEN CHOOSE A 4, 5, OR 6-DAY PLAN...

4-DAY PLAN

DAY 1 - RECORD

1. Record or reflect on the 6 W's (who, to whom, when, where, what genre, and why the passage was written).

2. Read through the passage a second time.

3. Record what the passage is about.

4. Note key and repeated words.

5. Record the main idea for the passage.

DAY 2 - EXPLORE

1. Read the passage in a different Bible translation.

2. Write down anything of significance the Holy Spirit draws your attention to.

3. Follow the cross-references and make a note of other places in Scripture that communicate a similar message.

DAY 3 - EXPLORE

1. Select and read at least one commentary on the passage. Take note of any new insights.

DAY 4 – APPLY & DO

1. Make notes on what the passage tells you about God.

2. Write down what the passage says about God's children.

3. Document the action God is prompting you to take.

4. Write down what you want to remember.

5-DAY PLAN

DAY 1 – RECORD

1. Record or reflect on the 6 W's (who, to whom, when, where, what genre, and why the passage was written).

2. Read through the passage a second time.

3. Record what the passage is about.

4. Note key and repeated words.

DAY 2 – RECORD

1. Record the main idea for the passage.

2. Read the passage in a different Bible translation.

3. Write down anything of significance the Holy Spirit draws your attention to.

DAY 3 – EXPLORE

1. Follow the cross-references and make a note of other places in Scripture that communicate a similar message.

DAY 4 – EXPLORE

1. Select and read at least one commentary on the passage. Take note of any new insights.

DAY 5 – APPLY & DO

1. Make notes on what the passage tells you about God.

2. Write down what the passage says about God's children.

3. Document the action God is prompting you to take.

4. Write down what you want to remember.

6-DAY PLAN

DAY 1 - RECORD

1. Record or reflect on the 6 W's (who, to whom, when, where, what genre, and why the passage was written).

2. Read through the passage a second time.

3. Record what the passage is about.

4. Note key and repeated words.

DAY 2 – RECORD

1. Record the main idea for the passage.

2. Read the passage in a different Bible translation.

3. Write down anything of significance the Holy Spirit draws your attention to.

DAY 3 – EXPLORE

1. Follow the cross-references and make a note of other places in Scripture that communicate a similar message.

DAY 4 – EXPLORE

1. Select and read at least one commentary on the passage. Take note of any new insights.

DAY 5 – APPLY

1. Make notes on what the passage tells you about God.

2. Write down what the passage says about God's children.

DAY 6 – DO

1. Document the action God is prompting you to take.

2. Write down what you want to remember.

PART 3

Additional Resources

Praying Scripture

Prayer is a crucial part of studying God's Word as we cannot understand without the help of the Holy Spirit. (See John 14:26.)

Here are some Scriptures you may want to use in your prayer time before and after studying.

EXAMPLES OF PRAYING SCRIPTURE:

Lord God, just as Psalm 19:14 says, I ask that the words of my mouth and the meditation of my heart be pleasing in your sight.

Father, God, help me to understand, obey, and observe your law with all my heart (Psalm 119:34).

God, use my time in your Word to transform and renew my mind so I may be able to discern your perfect will (Romans 12:2).

OTHER SCRIPTURES TO CONSIDER PRAYING:

Isaiah 55:11 NKJV— So shall My word be that goes forth from My mouth; It shall not return to Me void, But it shall accomplish what I please, And it shall prosper in the thing for which I sent it.

Psalm 119:34 NASB—Give me understanding, that I may observe Your law and keep it with all my heart.

Proverbs 2:1-5 ESV—My son, if you receive my words and treasure up my commandments with you, making your ear attentive to wisdom and inclining your heart to understanding; yes, if you call out for insight and raise your voice for understanding, if you seek it like silver and search for it as for hidden treasures, then you will understand the fear of the Lord and find the knowledge of God.

Psalm 19:14 NIV—May these words of my mouth and this meditation of my heart be pleasing in your sight, Lord, my Rock and my Redeemer.

Psalm 119:10-11 ESV—With my whole heart I seek you; let me not wander from your commandments! I have stored up your word in my heart, that I might not sin against you.

James 1:22-25 HCSB—But be doers of the word and not hearers only, deceiving yourselves. Because if anyone is a hearer of the word and not a doer, he is like a man looking at his own face in a mirror. For he looks at himself, goes away, and immediately forgets what kind of man he was. But the one who looks intently into the perfect law of freedom and perseveres in it, and is not a forgetful hearer but one who does good works—this person will be blessed in what he does.

Romans 12:2 HCSB—Do not be conformed to this age, but be transformed by the renewing of your mind, so that you may discern what is the good, pleasing, and perfect will of God.

Psalm 119:18 NIV—Open my eyes that I may see wonderful things in your law.

Psalm 119:105 KJV—Thy word is a lamp unto my feet, and a light unto my path.

2 Timothy 3:16-17 ESV—All Scripture is breathed out by God and profitable for teaching, for reproof, for correction, and for training in righteousness, that the man of God may be competent, equipped for every good work.

Hebrews 4:12 ESV—For the word of God is living and active, sharper than any two-edged sword, piercing to the division of soul and of spirit, of joints and of marrow, and discerning the thoughts and intentions of the heart.

Acts 4:13 NIV—When they saw the courage of Peter and John and realized that they were unschooled, ordinary men, they were astonished and they took note that these men had been with Jesus.

1 Peter 2:1-3 NIV—Therefore, rid yourselves of all malice and all deceit, hypocrisy, envy, and slander of every kind. Like newborn babies, crave pure spiritual milk, so that by it you may grow up in your salvation, now that you have tasted that the Lord is good.

Psalm 19:7-11 ESV—The law of the Lord is perfect, reviving the soul; the testimony of the Lord is sure, making wise the simple; the precepts of the Lord are right, rejoicing the heart; the commandment of the Lord is pure, enlightening the eyes; the fear of the Lord is clean, enduring forever; the rules of the Lord are true, and righteous altogether. More to be desired are they than gold, even much fine gold; sweeter also than honey and drippings of the honeycomb. Moreover, by them is your servant warned; in keeping them there is great reward.

Revelation 22:18-20 ESV—I warn everyone who hears the words of the prophecy of this book: If anyone adds anything to them, God will add to him the plagues described in this book. And if anyone takes words away from this book of prophecy, God will take away from him his share in the tree of life and in the holy city...

Joshua 1:8 HCSB—This book of instruction must not depart from your mouth; you are to recite it day and night so that you may carefully observe everything written in it. For then you will prosper and succeed in whatever you do.

Evaluating Resources

While God's Word is without error, the resources that we might use in studying the Bible may contain errors or may differ from our denominational teachings. So how can we discern whether a resource is reliable? How do we find resources that align with our beliefs? While this is not a foolproof method, these checks can protect us from false teachings and assist us in selecting resources that agree with our theology.

1. Before reading anything, we should pray and ask for guidance from the Holy Spirit.

If a spiritual "red flag" goes up, and you sense something doesn't seem quite right, investigate! Does this author believe differently than me, or is what they are saying biblically inaccurate? Just because you open a resource or start a book doesn't mean you have to finish it.

2. Test everything against the Scriptures.

This is the most important point: test everything against the Scriptures (not just one, but all of God's Word in its entirety). God's Word is always the authority. Always. See 1 John 4:1.

3. You need to know WHOM you are reading.

Is this an author you are familiar with? Do you know what his/her beliefs are on key biblical issues? Is this person credible in his/her field? Degrees are notable but not definitive. Does this person have experience with the topic s/he is writing or speaking upon?

4. Who recommended this resource to you?

Was this resource recommended by someone you know who has a strong walk with the Lord? Amazon reviews are not a reason to purchase a book or resource. Or maybe this was a book recommended by another author you admire. Keep in mind that book jackets and author recommendations are business-driven – put some weight, but not too much weight, on those recommendations.

Your church staff is an excellent resource for recommendations.

5. Review the sources.

Follow those footnotes and read the bibliography. Do you see the names of familiar books and authors that you know and trust?

6. Seek out wise counsel.

Ask a mentor or someone whose faith you admire if she has read the book or knows anything about the author. Email your pastor for input. Ask trusted leaders in your church for book recommendations. If the materials in your church bookstore or library are carefully vetted, check those shelves for books or resources.

7. Favor printed materials over the internet.

Publishers fact-check and extensively proof-read an author's work before publishing it, but that doesn't mean they are without error. Anyone can post anything on the internet – see #3.

ADDITIONAL THOUGHTS:

If someone is sharing an idea related to the Bible that is new or vastly different from what anyone else has ever written, treat it as suspect. While someone may find a fresh new way to explain something, rarely are there new revelations uncovered in God's Word.

The Bible warns us repeatedly about false teachers. Read 2 Peter 2:1-3, 1 John 4:1, 2 Timothy 4:3, Matthew 7:15-20, 2 Timothy 3:6-7, and Romans 16:17. While we don't need to hunt down false teachers, we do need to be aware of their presence.

Ideas for Going Deeper

If you find yourself with extra Bible study time or a desire to go deeper, you may wish to:

1. Memorize Scripture

You may want to choose one verse each week or a short passage to memorize before you complete your time in that book of the Bible.

2. Transcribe Scripture

Writing out the passage by hand is another way to allow God's Word to marinate in your mind. At the end of the week, write out the entire chapter by hand. I find as I do so, the Holy Spirit often shines a light on something I missed during my previous study sessions.

Frequently Asked Questions

HOW SHOULD I SELECT A BOOK OF THE BIBLE TO STUDY?

Spend time in prayer, asking God to point you to a particular book of Scripture. I've often found that God will place verses from the same book in my path repeatedly—during church services, over the radio, and even through social media. Even if you're unsure, pick one anyway. God will bless and use the time you've spent in His Word, no matter which of the 66 books you read.

If you're brand-new to Bible study, you may want to begin in the New Testament by studying Matthew, Mark, Luke, or John.

HOW MUCH TIME DOES IT TAKE TO COMPLETE THE HOMEWORK?

Most people complete the homework in about 10-20 minutes per day. Be sensitive to the Holy Spirit's prompting to dig deeper. Many people enjoy spending more time on the commentary section and following cross-references.

BESIDES A STUDY BIBLE AND A COMMENTARY, CAN I USE OTHER RESOURCES WHEN I COMPLETE THE READ WORKSHEETS?

You may find it helpful to use Bible dictionaries, Bible maps, or a concordance when completing the explore tasks. Like commentaries, these materials are written by Biblical scholars.

I suggest you do not use Bible study books, sermons, articles, or blog posts. While there are many authors and pastors who have much wisdom to share on the Scripture passage you are studying, it would be much like the telephone game. Most would be repeating material and information they discovered in Bible resources during their personal study time. There is no need to get that information second-hand. Go instead straight to the source!

CAN I USE THESE MATERIALS WITH MY SMALL GROUP?

To use the READ materials with your small group, each person will need to purchase their own copy of the book. Alternatively, you may want to use the READ Bible Study Kit for Groups. In addition to workbooks you may copy for participants, you'll also receive materials and resources for leading a small group using the READ Bible study method. You'll find more information at www.readbiblestudy.com.

PART 4

READ Weekly Worksheets

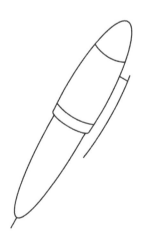

Date: _____ Passage: _____

RECORD (1st week) or RECALL (following weeks)

Who?	To whom?
When?	Where?
What genre?	Why?

RECORD what this passage is about.
(These notes are just for you—to help you capture the content of this passage.)

RECORD Repeated and Key Words:

RECORD the Main Idea (One Sentence or One Sentence per Section):

EXPLORE by reading the passage in at least one other translation.
(Note new insights and translation used.)

EXPLORE by making note of other places in Scripture that communicate a similar message.
(How does the passage connect to the passages before and after? How does the passage fit into the greater story of the Bible—creation, fall, redemption, restoration? Hint: Follow the cross-references in your Bible.)

EXPLORE by using at least one commentary to dig deeper.
(Examine the cultural and historical context.)

APPLY—What does the passage say about God?
(His character, His promises.)

APPLY—What does the passage say about God's children?
(Our responsibilities, our sin.)

DO—What does God want you to do today or this week to develop Christ-like character and habits?
(Is there something you need to pray about or confess? Whom do you need to forgive, encourage, or serve?)

DO—Remember—Use this space to make note of something you want to remember from your time in God's Word this week.
(What Bible verse was most significant to you during your time of study? What one thing do you want to be sure to remember?)

Date: _____ Passage: _____

RECORD (1st week) or RECALL (following weeks)

Who?	To whom?
When?	Where?
What genre?	Why?

RECORD what this passage is about.
(These notes are just for you—to help you capture the content of this passage.)

RECORD Repeated and Key Words:

RECORD the Main Idea (One Sentence or One Sentence per Section):

EXPLORE by reading the passage in at least one other translation.
(Note new insights and translation used.)

EXPLORE by making note of other places in Scripture that communicate a similar message.
(How does the passage connect to the passages before and after? How does the passage fit into the greater story of the Bible—creation, fall, redemption, restoration? Hint: Follow the cross-references in your Bible.)

EXPLORE by using at least one commentary to dig deeper.
(Examine the cultural and historical context.)

APPLY—What does the passage say about God?
(His character, His promises.)

APPLY—What does the passage say about God's children?
(Our responsibilities, our sin.)

DO—What does God want you to do today or this week to develop Christ-like character and habits?
(Is there something you need to pray about or confess? Whom do you need to forgive, encourage, or serve?)

DO—Remember—Use this space to make note of something you want to remember from your time in God's Word this week.
(What Bible verse was most significant to you during your time of study? What one thing do you want to be sure to remember?)

Date: _____ Passage: _____

RECORD (1st week) or RECALL (following weeks)

Who?	To whom?
When?	Where?
What genre?	Why?

RECORD what this passage is about.
(These notes are just for you—to help you capture the content of this passage.)

RECORD Repeated and Key Words:

RECORD the Main Idea (One Sentence or One Sentence per Section):

EXPLORE by reading the passage in at least one other translation.
(Note new insights and translation used.)

EXPLORE by making note of other places in Scripture that communicate a similar message.
(How does the passage connect to the passages before and after? How does the passage fit into the greater story of the Bible—creation, fall, redemption, restoration? Hint: Follow the cross-references in your Bible.)

EXPLORE by using at least one commentary to dig deeper.
(Examine the cultural and historical context.)

APPLY—What does the passage say about God?
(His character, His promises.)

APPLY—What does the passage say about God's children?
(Our responsibilities, our sin.)

DO—What does God want you to do today or this week to develop Christ-like character and habits?
(Is there something you need to pray about or confess? Whom do you need to forgive, encourage, or serve?)

DO—Remember—Use this space to make note of something you want to remember from your time in God's Word this week.
(What Bible verse was most significant to you during your time of study? What one thing do you want to be sure to remember?)

Date: _____ Passage: _____

RECORD (1st week) or RECALL (following weeks)

Who?	To whom?
When?	Where?
What genre?	Why?

RECORD what this passage is about.
(These notes are just for you—to help you capture the content of this passage.)

RECORD Repeated and Key Words:

RECORD the Main Idea (One Sentence or One Sentence per Section):

EXPLORE by reading the passage in at least one other translation.
(Note new insights and translation used.)

EXPLORE by making note of other places in Scripture that communicate a similar message.
(How does the passage connect to the passages before and after? How does the passage fit into the greater story of the Bible—creation, fall, redemption, restoration? Hint: Follow the cross-references in your Bible.)

EXPLORE by using at least one commentary to dig deeper.
(Examine the cultural and historical context.)

APPLY—What does the passage say about God?
(His character, His promises.)

APPLY—What does the passage say about God's children?
(Our responsibilities, our sin.)

DO—What does God want you to do today or this week to develop Christ-like character and habits?
(Is there something you need to pray about or confess? Whom do you need to forgive, encourage, or serve?)

DO—Remember—Use this space to make note of something you want to remember from your time in God's Word this week.
(What Bible verse was most significant to you during your time of study? What one thing do you want to be sure to remember?)

Date: _____ Passage: _____

RECORD (1st week) or RECALL (following weeks)

Who?	To whom?
When?	Where?
What genre?	Why?

RECORD what this passage is about.
(These notes are just for you—to help you capture the content of this passage.)

RECORD Repeated and Key Words:

RECORD the Main Idea (One Sentence or One Sentence per Section):

EXPLORE by reading the passage in at least one other translation.
(Note new insights and translation used.)

EXPLORE by making note of other places in Scripture that communicate a similar message.
(How does the passage connect to the passages before and after? How does the passage fit into the greater story of the Bible—creation, fall, redemption, restoration? Hint: Follow the cross-references in your Bible.)

EXPLORE by using at least one commentary to dig deeper.
(Examine the cultural and historical context.)

APPLY—What does the passage say about God?
(His character, His promises.)

APPLY—What does the passage say about God's children?
(Our responsibilities, our sin.)

DO—What does God want you to do today or this week to develop Christ-like character and habits?

(Is there something you need to pray about or confess? Whom do you need to forgive, encourage, or serve?)

DO—Remember—Use this space to make note of something you want to remember from your time in God's Word this week.

(What Bible verse was most significant to you during your time of study? What one thing do you want to be sure to remember?)

Date: _____ Passage: _____

RECORD (1st week) or RECALL (following weeks)

Who?	To whom?
When?	Where?
What genre?	Why?

RECORD what this passage is about.
(These notes are just for you—to help you capture the content of this passage.)

RECORD Repeated and Key Words:

RECORD the Main Idea (One Sentence or One Sentence per Section):

EXPLORE by reading the passage in at least one other translation.
(Note new insights and translation used.)

EXPLORE by making note of other places in Scripture that communicate a similar message.
(How does the passage connect to the passages before and after? How does the passage fit into the greater story of the Bible—creation, fall, redemption, restoration? Hint: Follow the cross-references in your Bible.)

EXPLORE by using at least one commentary to dig deeper.
(Examine the cultural and historical context.)

APPLY—What does the passage say about God?
(His character, His promises.)

APPLY—What does the passage say about God's children?
(Our responsibilities, our sin.)

DO—What does God want you to do today or this week to develop Christ-like character and habits?
(Is there something you need to pray about or confess? Whom do you need to forgive, encourage, or serve?)

DO—Remember—Use this space to make note of something you want to remember from your time in God's Word this week.
(What Bible verse was most significant to you during your time of study? What one thing do you want to be sure to remember?)

Date: _____ Passage: _____

RECORD (1st week) or RECALL (following weeks)

Who?	To whom?
When?	Where?
What genre?	Why?

RECORD what this passage is about.
(These notes are just for you—to help you capture the content of this passage.)

RECORD Repeated and Key Words:

RECORD the Main Idea (One Sentence or One Sentence per Section):

EXPLORE by reading the passage in at least one other translation.
(Note new insights and translation used.)

EXPLORE by making note of other places in Scripture that communicate a similar message.
(How does the passage connect to the passages before and after? How does the passage fit into the greater story of the Bible—creation, fall, redemption, restoration? Hint: Follow the cross-references in your Bible.)

EXPLORE by using at least one commentary to dig deeper.
(Examine the cultural and historical context.)

APPLY—What does the passage say about God?
(His character, His promises.)

APPLY—What does the passage say about God's children?
(Our responsibilities, our sin.)

DO—What does God want you to do today or this week to develop Christ-like character and habits?

(Is there something you need to pray about or confess? Whom do you need to forgive, encourage, or serve?)

DO—Remember—Use this space to make note of something you want to remember from your time in God's Word this week.

(What Bible verse was most significant to you during your time of study? What one thing do you want to be sure to remember?)

Date: _____ Passage: _____

RECORD (1st week) or RECALL (following weeks)

Who?	To whom?
When?	Where?
What genre?	Why?

RECORD what this passage is about.
(These notes are just for you—to help you capture the content of this passage.)

RECORD Repeated and Key Words:

RECORD the Main Idea (One Sentence or One Sentence per Section):

EXPLORE by reading the passage in at least one other translation.
(Note new insights and translation used.)

EXPLORE by making note of other places in Scripture that communicate a similar message.
(How does the passage connect to the passages before and after? How does the passage fit into the greater story of the Bible—creation, fall, redemption, restoration? Hint: Follow the cross-references in your Bible.)

EXPLORE by using at least one commentary to dig deeper.
(Examine the cultural and historical context.)

APPLY—What does the passage say about God?
(His character, His promises.)

APPLY—What does the passage say about God's children?
(Our responsibilities, our sin.)

DO—What does God want you to do today or this week to develop Christ-like character and habits?
(Is there something you need to pray about or confess? Whom do you need to forgive, encourage, or serve?)

DO—Remember—Use this space to make note of something you want to remember from your time in God's Word this week.
(What Bible verse was most significant to you during your time of study? What one thing do you want to be sure to remember?)

Date: _____ Passage: _____

RECORD (1st week) or RECALL (following weeks)

Who?	To whom?
When?	Where?
What genre?	Why?

RECORD what this passage is about.
(These notes are just for you—to help you capture the content of this passage.)

RECORD Repeated and Key Words:

RECORD the Main Idea (One Sentence or One Sentence per Section):

EXPLORE by reading the passage in at least one other translation.
(Note new insights and translation used.)

EXPLORE by making note of other places in Scripture that communicate a similar message.
(How does the passage connect to the passages before and after? How does the passage fit into the greater story of the Bible—creation, fall, redemption, restoration? Hint: Follow the cross-references in your Bible.)

EXPLORE by using at least one commentary to dig deeper.
(Examine the cultural and historical context.)

APPLY—What does the passage say about God?
(His character, His promises.)

APPLY—What does the passage say about God's children?
(Our responsibilities, our sin.)

DO—What does God want you to do today or this week to develop Christ-like character and habits?
(Is there something you need to pray about or confess? Whom do you need to forgive, encourage, or serve?)

DO—Remember—Use this space to make note of something you want to remember from your time in God's Word this week.
(What Bible verse was most significant to you during your time of study? What one thing do you want to be sure to remember?)

Date: _____ Passage: _____

RECORD (1st week) or RECALL (following weeks)

Who?	To whom?
When?	Where?
What genre?	Why?

RECORD what this passage is about.
(These notes are just for you—to help you capture the content of this passage.)

RECORD Repeated and Key Words:

RECORD the Main Idea (One Sentence or One Sentence per Section):

EXPLORE by reading the passage in at least one other translation.
(Note new insights and translation used.)

EXPLORE by making note of other places in Scripture that communicate a similar message.
(How does the passage connect to the passages before and after? How does the passage fit into the greater story of the Bible—creation, fall, redemption, restoration? Hint: Follow the cross-references in your Bible.)

EXPLORE by using at least one commentary to dig deeper.
(Examine the cultural and historical context.)

APPLY—What does the passage say about God?
(His character, His promises.)

APPLY—What does the passage say about God's children?
(Our responsibilities, our sin.)

DO—What does God want you to do today or this week to develop Christ-like character and habits?
(Is there something you need to pray about or confess? Whom do you need to forgive, encourage, or serve?)

DO—Remember—Use this space to make note of something you want to remember from your time in God's Word this week.
(What Bible verse was most significant to you during your time of study? What one thing do you want to be sure to remember?)

Date: _____ Passage: _____

RECORD (1st week) or RECALL (following weeks)

Who?	To whom?
When?	Where?
What genre?	Why?

RECORD what this passage is about.
(These notes are just for you—to help you capture the content of this passage.)

RECORD Repeated and Key Words:

RECORD the Main Idea (One Sentence or One Sentence per Section):

EXPLORE by reading the passage in at least one other translation.
(Note new insights and translation used.)

EXPLORE by making note of other places in Scripture that communicate a similar message.
(How does the passage connect to the passages before and after? How does the passage fit into the greater story of the Bible—creation, fall, redemption, restoration? Hint: Follow the cross-references in your Bible.)

EXPLORE by using at least one commentary to dig deeper.
(Examine the cultural and historical context.)

APPLY—What does the passage say about God?
(His character, His promises.)

APPLY—What does the passage say about God's children?
(Our responsibilities, our sin.)

DO—What does God want you to do today or this week to develop Christ-like character and habits?
(Is there something you need to pray about or confess? Whom do you need to forgive, encourage, or serve?)

DO—Remember—Use this space to make note of something you want to remember from your time in God's Word this week.
(What Bible verse was most significant to you during your time of study? What one thing do you want to be sure to remember?)

Date: _____ Passage: _____

RECORD (1st week) or RECALL (following weeks)

Who?	To whom?
When?	Where?
What genre?	Why?

RECORD what this passage is about.
(These notes are just for you—to help you capture the content of this passage.)

RECORD Repeated and Key Words:

RECORD the Main Idea (One Sentence or One Sentence per Section):

EXPLORE by reading the passage in at least one other translation.
(Note new insights and translation used.)

EXPLORE by making note of other places in Scripture that communicate a similar message.
(How does the passage connect to the passages before and after? How does the passage fit into the greater story of the Bible—creation, fall, redemption, restoration? Hint: Follow the cross-references in your Bible.)

EXPLORE by using at least one commentary to dig deeper.
(Examine the cultural and historical context.)

APPLY—What does the passage say about God?
(His character, His promises.)

APPLY—What does the passage say about God's children?
(Our responsibilities, our sin.)

DO—What does God want you to do today or this week to develop Christ-like character and habits?
(Is there something you need to pray about or confess? Whom do you need to forgive, encourage, or serve?)

DO—Remember—Use this space to make note of something you want to remember from your time in God's Word this week.
(What Bible verse was most significant to you during your time of study? What one thing do you want to be sure to remember?)

Date: _____ Passage: _____

RECORD (1st week) or RECALL (following weeks)

Who?	To whom?
When?	Where?
What genre?	Why?

RECORD what this passage is about.
(These notes are just for you—to help you capture the content of this passage.)

RECORD Repeated and Key Words:

RECORD the Main Idea (One Sentence or One Sentence per Section):

EXPLORE by reading the passage in at least one other translation.
(Note new insights and translation used.)

EXPLORE by making note of other places in Scripture that communicate a similar message.
(How does the passage connect to the passages before and after? How does the passage fit into the greater story of the Bible—creation, fall, redemption, restoration? Hint: Follow the cross-references in your Bible.)

EXPLORE by using at least one commentary to dig deeper.
(Examine the cultural and historical context.)

APPLY—What does the passage say about God?
(His character, His promises.)

APPLY—What does the passage say about God's children?
(Our responsibilities, our sin.)

DO—What does God want you to do today or this week to develop Christ-like character and habits?
(Is there something you need to pray about or confess? Whom do you need to forgive, encourage, or serve?)

DO—Remember—Use this space to make note of something you want to remember from your time in God's Word this week.
(What Bible verse was most significant to you during your time of study? What one thing do you want to be sure to remember?)

Date: _____ Passage: _____

RECORD (1st week) or RECALL (following weeks)

Who?	To whom?
When?	Where?
What genre?	Why?

RECORD what this passage is about.
(These notes are just for you—to help you capture the content of this passage.)

RECORD Repeated and Key Words:

RECORD the Main Idea (One Sentence or One Sentence per Section):

EXPLORE by reading the passage in at least one other translation.
(Note new insights and translation used.)

EXPLORE by making note of other places in Scripture that communicate a similar message.
(How does the passage connect to the passages before and after? How does the passage fit into the greater story of the Bible—creation, fall, redemption, restoration? Hint: Follow the cross-references in your Bible.)

EXPLORE by using at least one commentary to dig deeper.
(Examine the cultural and historical context.)

APPLY—What does the passage say about God?
(His character, His promises.)

APPLY—What does the passage say about God's children?
(Our responsibilities, our sin.)

DO—What does God want you to do today or this week to develop Christ-like character and habits?
(Is there something you need to pray about or confess? Whom do you need to forgive, encourage, or serve?)

DO—Remember—Use this space to make note of something you want to remember from your time in God's Word this week.
(What Bible verse was most significant to you during your time of study? What one thing do you want to be sure to remember?)

Date: _____ Passage: _____

RECORD (1st week) or RECALL (following weeks)

Who?	To whom?
When?	Where?
What genre?	Why?

RECORD what this passage is about.
(These notes are just for you—to help you capture the content of this passage.)

RECORD Repeated and Key Words:

RECORD the Main Idea (One Sentence or One Sentence per Section):

EXPLORE by reading the passage in at least one other translation.
(Note new insights and translation used.)

EXPLORE by making note of other places in Scripture that communicate a similar message.
(How does the passage connect to the passages before and after? How does the passage fit into the greater story of the Bible—creation, fall, redemption, restoration? Hint: Follow the cross-references in your Bible.)

EXPLORE by using at least one commentary to dig deeper.
(Examine the cultural and historical context.)

APPLY—What does the passage say about God?
(His character, His promises.)

APPLY—What does the passage say about God's children?
(Our responsibilities, our sin.)

DO—What does God want you to do today or this week to develop Christ-like character and habits?
(Is there something you need to pray about or confess? Whom do you need to forgive, encourage, or serve?)

DO—Remember—Use this space to make note of something you want to remember from your time in God's Word this week.
(What Bible verse was most significant to you during your time of study? What one thing do you want to be sure to remember?)

Date: _____ Passage: _____

RECORD (1st week) or RECALL (following weeks)

Who?	To whom?
When?	Where?
What genre?	Why?

RECORD what this passage is about.
(These notes are just for you—to help you capture the content of this passage.)

RECORD Repeated and Key Words:

RECORD the Main Idea (One Sentence or One Sentence per Section):

EXPLORE by reading the passage in at least one other translation.
(Note new insights and translation used.)

EXPLORE by making note of other places in Scripture that communicate a similar message.
(How does the passage connect to the passages before and after? How does the passage fit into the greater story of the Bible—creation, fall, redemption, restoration? Hint: Follow the cross-references in your Bible.)

EXPLORE by using at least one commentary to dig deeper.
(Examine the cultural and historical context.)

APPLY—What does the passage say about God?
(His character, His promises.)

APPLY—What does the passage say about God's children?
(Our responsibilities, our sin.)

DO—What does God want you to do today or this week to develop Christ-like character and habits?
(Is there something you need to pray about or confess? Whom do you need to forgive, encourage, or serve?)

DO—Remember—Use this space to make note of something you want to remember from your time in God's Word this week.
(What Bible verse was most significant to you during your time of study? What one thing do you want to be sure to remember?)

Date: _____ Passage: _____

RECORD (1st week) or RECALL (following weeks)

Who?	To whom?
When?	Where?
What genre?	Why?

RECORD what this passage is about.
(These notes are just for you—to help you capture the content of this passage.)

RECORD Repeated and Key Words:

RECORD the Main Idea (One Sentence or One Sentence per Section):

EXPLORE by reading the passage in at least one other translation.
(Note new insights and translation used.)

EXPLORE by making note of other places in Scripture that communicate a similar message.
(How does the passage connect to the passages before and after? How does the passage fit into the greater story of the Bible—creation, fall, redemption, restoration? Hint: Follow the cross-references in your Bible.)

EXPLORE by using at least one commentary to dig deeper.
(Examine the cultural and historical context.)

APPLY—What does the passage say about God?
(His character, His promises.)

APPLY—What does the passage say about God's children?
(Our responsibilities, our sin.)

DO—What does God want you to do today or this week to develop Christ-like character and habits?
(Is there something you need to pray about or confess? Whom do you need to forgive, encourage, or serve?)

DO—Remember—Use this space to make note of something you want to remember from your time in God's Word this week.
(What Bible verse was most significant to you during your time of study? What one thing do you want to be sure to remember?)

Date: _____ Passage: _____

RECORD (1st week) or RECALL (following weeks)

Who?	To whom?
When?	Where?
What genre?	Why?

RECORD what this passage is about.
(These notes are just for you—to help you capture the content of this passage.)

RECORD Repeated and Key Words:

RECORD the Main Idea (One Sentence or One Sentence per Section):

EXPLORE by reading the passage in at least one other translation.
(Note new insights and translation used.)

EXPLORE by making note of other places in Scripture that communicate a similar message.
(How does the passage connect to the passages before and after? How does the passage fit into the greater story of the Bible—creation, fall, redemption, restoration? Hint: Follow the cross-references in your Bible.)

EXPLORE by using at least one commentary to dig deeper.
(Examine the cultural and historical context.)

APPLY—What does the passage say about God?
(His character, His promises.)

APPLY—What does the passage say about God's children?
(Our responsibilities, our sin.)

DO—What does God want you to do today or this week to develop Christ-like character and habits?
(Is there something you need to pray about or confess? Whom do you need to forgive, encourage, or serve?)

DO—Remember—Use this space to make note of something you want to remember from your time in God's Word this week.
(What Bible verse was most significant to you during your time of study? What one thing do you want to be sure to remember?)

Date: _____ Passage: _____

RECORD (1st week) or RECALL (following weeks)

Who?	To whom?
When?	Where?
What genre?	Why?

RECORD what this passage is about.
(These notes are just for you—to help you capture the content of this passage.)

RECORD Repeated and Key Words:

RECORD the Main Idea (One Sentence or One Sentence per Section):

EXPLORE by reading the passage in at least one other translation.
(Note new insights and translation used.)

EXPLORE by making note of other places in Scripture that communicate a similar message.
(How does the passage connect to the passages before and after? How does the passage fit into the greater story of the Bible—creation, fall, redemption, restoration? Hint: Follow the cross-references in your Bible.)

EXPLORE by using at least one commentary to dig deeper.
(Examine the cultural and historical context.)

APPLY—What does the passage say about God?
(His character, His promises.)

APPLY—What does the passage say about God's children?
(Our responsibilities, our sin.)

DO—What does God want you to do today or this week to develop Christ-like character and habits?
(Is there something you need to pray about or confess? Whom do you need to forgive, encourage, or serve?)

DO—Remember—Use this space to make note of something you want to remember from your time in God's Word this week.
(What Bible verse was most significant to you during your time of study? What one thing do you want to be sure to remember?)

Date: _____ Passage: _____

RECORD (1st week) or RECALL (following weeks)

Who?	To whom?
When?	Where?
What genre?	Why?

RECORD what this passage is about.
(These notes are just for you—to help you capture the content of this passage.)

RECORD Repeated and Key Words:

RECORD the Main Idea (One Sentence or One Sentence per Section):

EXPLORE by reading the passage in at least one other translation.
(Note new insights and translation used.)

EXPLORE by making note of other places in Scripture that communicate a similar message.
(How does the passage connect to the passages before and after? How does the passage fit into the greater story of the Bible—creation, fall, redemption, restoration? Hint: Follow the cross-references in your Bible.)

EXPLORE by using at least one commentary to dig deeper.
(Examine the cultural and historical context.)

APPLY—What does the passage say about God?
(His character, His promises.)

APPLY—What does the passage say about God's children?
(Our responsibilities, our sin.)

DO—What does God want you to do today or this week to develop Christ-like character and habits?
(Is there something you need to pray about or confess? Whom do you need to forgive, encourage, or serve?)

DO—Remember—Use this space to make note of something you want to remember from your time in God's Word this week.
(What Bible verse was most significant to you during your time of study? What one thing do you want to be sure to remember?)

Date: _____ Passage: _____

RECORD (1st week) or RECALL (following weeks)

Who?	To whom?
When?	Where?
What genre?	Why?

RECORD what this passage is about.
(These notes are just for you—to help you capture the content of this passage.)

RECORD Repeated and Key Words:

RECORD the Main Idea (One Sentence or One Sentence per Section):

EXPLORE by reading the passage in at least one other translation.
(Note new insights and translation used.)

EXPLORE by making note of other places in Scripture that communicate a similar message.
(How does the passage connect to the passages before and after? How does the passage fit into the greater story of the Bible—creation, fall, redemption, restoration? Hint: Follow the cross-references in your Bible.)

138

EXPLORE by using at least one commentary to dig deeper.
(Examine the cultural and historical context.)

APPLY—What does the passage say about God?
(His character, His promises.)

APPLY—What does the passage say about God's children?
(Our responsibilities, our sin.)

DO—What does God want you to do today or this week to develop Christ-like character and habits?

(Is there something you need to pray about or confess? Whom do you need to forgive, encourage, or serve?)

DO—Remember—Use this space to make note of something you want to remember from your time in God's Word this week.

(What Bible verse was most significant to you during your time of study? What one thing do you want to be sure to remember?)

Date: _____ Passage: _____

RECORD (1st week) or RECALL (following weeks)

Who?	To whom?
When?	Where?
What genre?	Why?

RECORD what this passage is about.
(These notes are just for you—to help you capture the content of this passage.)

RECORD Repeated and Key Words:

RECORD the Main Idea (One Sentence or One Sentence per Section):

EXPLORE by reading the passage in at least one other translation.
(Note new insights and translation used.)

EXPLORE by making note of other places in Scripture that communicate a similar message.
(How does the passage connect to the passages before and after? How does the passage fit into the greater story of the Bible—creation, fall, redemption, restoration? Hint: Follow the cross-references in your Bible.)

142

EXPLORE by using at least one commentary to dig deeper.
(Examine the cultural and historical context.)

APPLY—What does the passage say about God?
(His character, His promises.)

APPLY—What does the passage say about God's children?
(Our responsibilities, our sin.)

DO—What does God want you to do today or this week to develop Christ-like character and habits?
(Is there something you need to pray about or confess? Whom do you need to forgive, encourage, or serve?)

DO—Remember—Use this space to make note of something you want to remember from your time in God's Word this week.
(What Bible verse was most significant to you during your time of study? What one thing do you want to be sure to remember?)

Date: _____ Passage: _____

RECORD (1st week) or RECALL (following weeks)

Who?	To whom?
When?	Where?
What genre?	Why?

RECORD what this passage is about.
(These notes are just for you—to help you capture the content of this passage.)

RECORD Repeated and Key Words:

RECORD the Main Idea (One Sentence or One Sentence per Section):

EXPLORE by reading the passage in at least one other translation.
(Note new insights and translation used.)

EXPLORE by making note of other places in Scripture that communicate a similar message.
(How does the passage connect to the passages before and after? How does the passage fit into the greater story of the Bible—creation, fall, redemption, restoration? Hint: Follow the cross-references in your Bible.)

EXPLORE by using at least one commentary to dig deeper.
(Examine the cultural and historical context.)

APPLY—What does the passage say about God?
(His character, His promises.)

APPLY—What does the passage say about God's children?
(Our responsibilities, our sin.)

DO—What does God want you to do today or this week to develop Christ-like character and habits?
(Is there something you need to pray about or confess? Whom do you need to forgive, encourage, or serve?)

DO—Remember—Use this space to make note of something you want to remember from your time in God's Word this week.
(What Bible verse was most significant to you during your time of study? What one thing do you want to be sure to remember?)

Date: _____ Passage: _____

RECORD (1st week) or RECALL (following weeks)

Who?	To whom?
When?	Where?
What genre?	Why?

RECORD what this passage is about.
(These notes are just for you—to help you capture the content of this passage.)

RECORD Repeated and Key Words:

RECORD the Main Idea (One Sentence or One Sentence per Section):

EXPLORE by reading the passage in at least one other translation.
(Note new insights and translation used.)

EXPLORE by making note of other places in Scripture that communicate a similar message.
(How does the passage connect to the passages before and after? How does the passage fit into the greater story of the Bible—creation, fall, redemption, restoration? Hint: Follow the cross-references in your Bible.)

EXPLORE by using at least one commentary to dig deeper.
(Examine the cultural and historical context.)

APPLY—What does the passage say about God?
(His character, His promises.)

APPLY—What does the passage say about God's children?
(Our responsibilities, our sin.)

DO—What does God want you to do today or this week to develop Christ-like character and habits?
(Is there something you need to pray about or confess? Whom do you need to forgive, encourage, or serve?)

DO—Remember—Use this space to make note of something you want to remember from your time in God's Word this week.
(What Bible verse was most significant to you during your time of study? What one thing do you want to be sure to remember?)

Date: _____ Passage: _____

RECORD (1st week) or RECALL (following weeks)

Who?	To whom?
When?	Where?
What genre?	Why?

RECORD what this passage is about.
(These notes are just for you—to help you capture the content of this passage.)

RECORD Repeated and Key Words:

RECORD the Main Idea (One Sentence or One Sentence per Section):

EXPLORE by reading the passage in at least one other translation.
(Note new insights and translation used.)

EXPLORE by making note of other places in Scripture that communicate a similar message.
(How does the passage connect to the passages before and after? How does the passage fit into the greater story of the Bible—creation, fall, redemption, restoration? Hint: Follow the cross-references in your Bible.)

EXPLORE by using at least one commentary to dig deeper.
(Examine the cultural and historical context.)

APPLY—What does the passage say about God?
(His character, His promises.)

APPLY—What does the passage say about God's children?
(Our responsibilities, our sin.)

DO—What does God want you to do today or this week to develop Christ-like character and habits?
(Is there something you need to pray about or confess? Whom do you need to forgive, encourage, or serve?)

DO—Remember—Use this space to make note of something you want to remember from your time in God's Word this week.
(What Bible verse was most significant to you during your time of study? What one thing do you want to be sure to remember?)

156

Date: _____ Passage: _____

RECORD (1st week) or RECALL (following weeks)

Who?	To whom?
When?	Where?
What genre?	Why?

RECORD what this passage is about.
(These notes are just for you—to help you capture the content of this passage.)

RECORD Repeated and Key Words:

RECORD the Main Idea (One Sentence or One Sentence per Section):

EXPLORE by reading the passage in at least one other translation.
(Note new insights and translation used.)

EXPLORE by making note of other places in Scripture that communicate a similar message.
(How does the passage connect to the passages before and after? How does the passage fit into the greater story of the Bible—creation, fall, redemption, restoration? Hint: Follow the cross-references in your Bible.)

EXPLORE by using at least one commentary to dig deeper.
(Examine the cultural and historical context.)

APPLY—What does the passage say about God?
(His character, His promises.)

APPLY—What does the passage say about God's children?
(Our responsibilities, our sin.)

DO—What does God want you to do today or this week to develop Christ-like character and habits?
(Is there something you need to pray about or confess? Whom do you need to forgive, encourage, or serve?)

DO—Remember—Use this space to make note of something you want to remember from your time in God's Word this week.
(What Bible verse was most significant to you during your time of study? What one thing do you want to be sure to remember?)

Date: _____ Passage: _____

RECORD (1st week) or RECALL (following weeks)

Who?	To whom?
When?	Where?
What genre?	Why?

RECORD what this passage is about.
(These notes are just for you—to help you capture the content of this passage.)

RECORD Repeated and Key Words:

RECORD the Main Idea (One Sentence or One Sentence per Section):

EXPLORE by reading the passage in at least one other translation.
(Note new insights and translation used.)

EXPLORE by making note of other places in Scripture that communicate a similar message.
(How does the passage connect to the passages before and after? How does the passage fit into the greater story of the Bible—creation, fall, redemption, restoration? Hint: Follow the cross-references in your Bible.)

EXPLORE by using at least one commentary to dig deeper.
(Examine the cultural and historical context.)

APPLY—What does the passage say about God?
(His character, His promises.)

APPLY—What does the passage say about God's children?
(Our responsibilities, our sin.)

DO—What does God want you to do today or this week to develop Christ-like character and habits?
(Is there something you need to pray about or confess? Whom do you need to forgive, encourage, or serve?)

DO—Remember—Use this space to make note of something you want to remember from your time in God's Word this week.
(What Bible verse was most significant to you during your time of study? What one thing do you want to be sure to remember?)

Date: _____ Passage: _____

RECORD (1st week) or RECALL (following weeks)

Who?	To whom?
When?	Where?
What genre?	Why?

RECORD what this passage is about.
(These notes are just for you—to help you capture the content of this passage.)

RECORD Repeated and Key Words:

RECORD the Main Idea (One Sentence or One Sentence per Section):

EXPLORE by reading the passage in at least one other translation.
(Note new insights and translation used.)

EXPLORE by making note of other places in Scripture that communicate a
similar message.
*(How does the passage connect to the passages before and after? How does
the passage fit into the greater story of the Bible—creation, fall, redemption,
restoration? Hint: Follow the cross-references in your Bible.)*

EXPLORE by using at least one commentary to dig deeper.
(Examine the cultural and historical context.)

APPLY—What does the passage say about God?
(His character, His promises.)

APPLY—What does the passage say about God's children?
(Our responsibilities, our sin.)

DO—What does God want you to do today or this week to develop Christ-like character and habits?
(Is there something you need to pray about or confess? Whom do you need to forgive, encourage, or serve?)

DO—Remember—Use this space to make note of something you want to remember from your time in God's Word this week.
(What Bible verse was most significant to you during your time of study? What one thing do you want to be sure to remember?)

Date: _____ Passage: _____

RECORD (1st week) or RECALL (following weeks)

Who?	To whom?
When?	Where?
What genre?	Why?

RECORD what this passage is about.
(These notes are just for you—to help you capture the content of this passage.)

RECORD Repeated and Key Words:

RECORD the Main Idea (One Sentence or One Sentence per Section):

EXPLORE by reading the passage in at least one other translation.
(Note new insights and translation used.)

EXPLORE by making note of other places in Scripture that communicate a similar message.
(How does the passage connect to the passages before and after? How does the passage fit into the greater story of the Bible—creation, fall, redemption, restoration? Hint: Follow the cross-references in your Bible.)

EXPLORE by using at least one commentary to dig deeper.
(Examine the cultural and historical context.)

APPLY—What does the passage say about God?
(His character, His promises.)

APPLY—What does the passage say about God's children?
(Our responsibilities, our sin.)

DO—What does God want you to do today or this week to develop Christ-like character and habits?
(Is there something you need to pray about or confess? Whom do you need to forgive, encourage, or serve?)

DO—Remember—Use this space to make note of something you want to remember from your time in God's Word this week.
(What Bible verse was most significant to you during your time of study? What one thing do you want to be sure to remember?)

Date: _____ Passage: _____

RECORD (1st week) or RECALL (following weeks)

Who?	To whom?
When?	Where?
What genre?	Why?

RECORD what this passage is about.
(These notes are just for you—to help you capture the content of this passage.)

RECORD Repeated and Key Words:

RECORD the Main Idea (One Sentence or One Sentence per Section):

EXPLORE by reading the passage in at least one other translation.
(Note new insights and translation used.)

EXPLORE by making note of other places in Scripture that communicate a similar message.
(How does the passage connect to the passages before and after? How does the passage fit into the greater story of the Bible—creation, fall, redemption, restoration? Hint: Follow the cross-references in your Bible.)

EXPLORE by using at least one commentary to dig deeper.
(Examine the cultural and historical context.)

APPLY—What does the passage say about God?
(His character, His promises.)

APPLY—What does the passage say about God's children?
(Our responsibilities, our sin.)

DO—What does God want you to do today or this week to develop Christ-like character and habits?
(Is there something you need to pray about or confess? Whom do you need to forgive, encourage, or serve?)

DO—Remember—Use this space to make note of something you want to remember from your time in God's Word this week.
(What Bible verse was most significant to you during your time of study? What one thing do you want to be sure to remember?)

PART 5

READ Reflection Worksheets

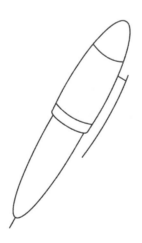

READ Reflections on the Book of_____

Before completing this worksheet, pray and take a fresh look at the book in its entirety by reading it from start to finish.

RECORD

What were the repeated words and ideas in this book of the Bible?

Summarize this book of the Bible in one sentence.

If you had to choose just one word, what word would you use to describe this book of the Bible?

What do you want others to know about this book of the Bible?

EXPLORE

Flip back through your notes and your Bible in search of verses you recorded or highlighted.

Which verse(s) did God specifically and personally draw to your attention during your study? Choose at least two and write them below. Challenge yourself to memorize one of the verses you've noted.

What is something you may not have understood without the help of a commentary or cross-reference?

APPLY

What new things have you learned about God?

Perhaps an attribute of His character, a new fact you discovered, or something you knew but appreciate more now.

What new things have you learned about God's children during your study of this book of the Bible?

DO

Describe an action, step of faith, or act of obedience you have taken or God is prompting you to take as a result of this study.

READ Reflections on the Book of_____

Before completing this worksheet, pray and take a fresh look at the book in its entirety by reading it from start to finish.

RECORD

What were the repeated words and ideas in this book of the Bible?

Summarize this book of the Bible in one sentence.

If you had to choose just one word, what word would you use to describe this book of the Bible?

What do you want others to know about this book of the Bible?

EXPLORE

Flip back through your notes and your Bible in search of verses you recorded or highlighted.

Which verse(s) did God specifically and personally draw to your attention during your study? Choose at least two and write them below. Challenge yourself to memorize one of the verses you've noted.

What is something you may not have understood without the help of a commentary or cross-reference?

APPLY

What new things have you learned about God?

Perhaps an attribute of His character, a new fact you discovered, or something you knew but appreciate more now.

What new things have you learned about God's children during your study of this book of the Bible?

DO

Describe an action, step of faith, or act of obedience you have taken or God is prompting you to take as a result of this study.

READ Reflections on the Book of_____

Before completing this worksheet, pray and take a fresh look at the book in its entirety by reading it from start to finish.

RECORD

What were the repeated words and ideas in this book of the Bible?

Summarize this book of the Bible in one sentence.

If you had to choose just one word, what word would you use to describe this book of the Bible?

What do you want others to know about this book of the Bible?

EXPLORE

Flip back through your notes and your Bible in search of verses you recorded or highlighted.

Which verse(s) did God specifically and personally draw to your attention during your study? Choose at least two and write them below. Challenge yourself to memorize one of the verses you've noted.

What is something you may not have understood without the help of a commentary or cross-reference?

186

APPLY

What new things have you learned about God?

Perhaps an attribute of His character, a new fact you discovered, or something you knew but appreciate more now.

What new things have you learned about God's children during your study of this book of the Bible?

DO

Describe an action, step of faith, or act of obedience you have taken or God is prompting you to take as a result of this study.

READ Reflections on the Book of_____

Before completing this worksheet, pray and take a fresh look at the book in its entirety by reading it from start to finish.

RECORD
What were the repeated words and ideas in this book of the Bible?

Summarize this book of the Bible in one sentence.

If you had to choose just one word, what word would you use to describe this book of the Bible?

What do you want others to know about this book of the Bible?

EXPLORE

Flip back through your notes and your Bible in search of verses you recorded or highlighted.

Which verse(s) did God specifically and personally draw to your attention during your study? Choose at least two and write them below. Challenge yourself to memorize one of the verses you've noted.

What is something you may not have understood without the help of a commentary or cross-reference?

APPLY

What new things have you learned about God?

Perhaps an attribute of His character, a new fact you discovered, or something you knew but appreciate more now.

What new things have you learned about God's children during your study of this book of the Bible?

DO

Describe an action, step of faith, or act of obedience you have taken or God is prompting you to take as a result of this study.

READ Reflections on the Book of_____

Before completing this worksheet, pray and take a fresh look at the book in its entirety by reading it from start to finish.

RECORD

What were the repeated words and ideas in this book of the Bible?

Summarize this book of the Bible in one sentence.

If you had to choose just one word, what word would you use to describe this book of the Bible?

What do you want others to know about this book of the Bible?

EXPLORE

Flip back through your notes and your Bible in search of verses you recorded or highlighted.

Which verse(s) did God specifically and personally draw to your attention during your study? Choose at least two and write them below. Challenge yourself to memorize one of the verses you've noted.

What is something you may not have understood without the help of a commentary or cross-reference?

APPLY

What new things have you learned about God?

Perhaps an attribute of His character, a new fact you discovered, or something you knew but appreciate more now.

What new things have you learned about God's children during your study of this book of the Bible?

DO

Describe an action, step of faith, or act of obedience you have taken or God is prompting you to take as a result of this study.

READ Reflections on the Book of_____

Before completing this worksheet, pray and take a fresh look at the book in its entirety by reading it from start to finish.

RECORD

What were the repeated words and ideas in this book of the Bible?

Summarize this book of the Bible in one sentence.

If you had to choose just one word, what word would you use to describe this book of the Bible?

What do you want others to know about this book of the Bible?

EXPLORE

Flip back through your notes and your Bible in search of verses you recorded or highlighted.

Which verse(s) did God specifically and personally draw to your attention during your study? Choose at least two and write them below. Challenge yourself to memorize one of the verses you've noted.

What is something you may not have understood without the help of a commentary or cross-reference?

APPLY

What new things have you learned about God?

Perhaps an attribute of His character, a new fact you discovered, or something you knew but appreciate more now.

What new things have you learned about God's children during your study of this book of the Bible?

DO

Describe an action, step of faith, or act of obedience you have taken or God is prompting you to take as a result of this study.

READ Reflections on the Book of_____

Before completing this worksheet, pray and take a fresh look at the book in its entirety by reading it from start to finish.

RECORD

What were the repeated words and ideas in this book of the Bible?

Summarize this book of the Bible in one sentence.

If you had to choose just one word, what word would you use to describe this book of the Bible?

What do you want others to know about this book of the Bible?

EXPLORE

Flip back through your notes and your Bible in search of verses you recorded or highlighted.

Which verse(s) did God specifically and personally draw to your attention during your study? Choose at least two and write them below. Challenge yourself to memorize one of the verses you've noted.

What is something you may not have understood without the help of a commentary or cross-reference?

APPLY

What new things have you learned about God?

Perhaps an attribute of His character, a new fact you discovered, or something you knew but appreciate more now.

What new things have you learned about God's children during your study of this book of the Bible?

DO

Describe an action, step of faith, or act of obedience you have taken or God is prompting you to take as a result of this study.

READ Reflections on the Book of_____

Before completing this worksheet, pray and take a fresh look at the book in its entirety by reading it from start to finish.

RECORD

What were the repeated words and ideas in this book of the Bible?

Summarize this book of the Bible in one sentence.

If you had to choose just one word, what word would you use to describe this book of the Bible?

What do you want others to know about this book of the Bible?

EXPLORE

Flip back through your notes and your Bible in search of verses you recorded or highlighted.

Which verse(s) did God specifically and personally draw to your attention during your study? Choose at least two and write them below. Challenge yourself to memorize one of the verses you've noted.

What is something you may not have understood without the help of a commentary or cross-reference?

APPLY

What new things have you learned about God?

Perhaps an attribute of His character, a new fact you discovered, or something you knew but appreciate more now.

What new things have you learned about God's children during your study of this book of the Bible?

DO

Describe an action, step of faith, or act of obedience you have taken or God is prompting you to take as a result of this study.

READ Reflections on the Book of_____

Before completing this worksheet, pray and take a fresh look at the book in its entirety by reading it from start to finish.

RECORD

What were the repeated words and ideas in this book of the Bible?

Summarize this book of the Bible in one sentence.

If you had to choose just one word, what word would you use to describe this book of the Bible?

What do you want others to know about this book of the Bible?

EXPLORE

Flip back through your notes and your Bible in search of verses you recorded or highlighted.

Which verse(s) did God specifically and personally draw to your attention during your study? Choose at least two and write them below. Challenge yourself to memorize one of the verses you've noted.

What is something you may not have understood without the help of a commentary or cross-reference?

APPLY

What new things have you learned about God?

Perhaps an attribute of His character, a new fact you discovered, or something you knew but appreciate more now.

What new things have you learned about God's children during your study of this book of the Bible?

DO

Describe an action, step of faith, or act of obedience you have taken or God is prompting you to take as a result of this study.

READ Reflections on the Book of_____

Before completing this worksheet, pray and take a fresh look at the book in its entirety by reading it from start to finish.

RECORD
What were the repeated words and ideas in this book of the Bible?

Summarize this book of the Bible in one sentence.

If you had to choose just one word, what word would you use to describe this book of the Bible?

What do you want others to know about this book of the Bible?

EXPLORE

Flip back through your notes and your Bible in search of verses you recorded or highlighted.

Which verse(s) did God specifically and personally draw to your attention during your study? Choose at least two and write them below. Challenge yourself to memorize one of the verses you've noted.

What is something you may not have understood without the help of a commentary or cross-reference?

APPLY

What new things have you learned about God?

Perhaps an attribute of His character, a new fact you discovered, or something you knew but appreciate more now.

What new things have you learned about God's children during your study of this book of the Bible?

DO

Describe an action, step of faith, or act of obedience you have taken or God is prompting you to take as a result of this study.

Acknowledgements

I am so thankful the Lord led me on the adventure of learning to study God's Word on my own. The regular practice of READing God's Word has not only increased my knowledge, but my love for my Savior has grown.

To my husband, Sean, and our boys, Nick and Cam, thank you for encouraging me to study God's Word and for waiting patiently so many times for me to finish my Bible study time. I pray you'll always hunger for God's Word.

Thank you Denise and the women of Independence Baptist Hill Church for being the guinea pigs for the first READ Bible study group sessions. Digging into God's Word alongside each one of you was a joy and a privilege. Watching your confidence and ability to study God's Word flourish was a gift.

Jewel, Linda, and Rochelle, thank you for your input on the latest rounds of edits on the READ Bible Study Workbook. Your experience and insight were incredibly helpful.

To all those who have provided a platform for me to share about studying God's Word, thank you for allowing me the opportunity to encourage your group to dig deep and study the Scriptures. I pray your groups will treasure God's Word today and always.

About the Author

Cyndee Ownbey is the author of *Rethinking Women's Ministry: Biblical, Practical Tools for Cultivating a Flourishing Community*. She is a mentor to thousands of women's ministry leaders through her website and Facebook community, Women's Ministry Toolbox. A seasoned Bible study teacher, Cyndee has taught hundreds of women how to use the READ Bible study format in Bible study groups and at conferences. She is passionate about teaching women and leaders how to study the Bible on their own.

Over the years, God has expanded the reach of Women's Ministry Toolbox to include a Facebook group of over 4000 women's ministry leaders, an online classroom featuring women's ministry training, and several printable women's ministry resources.

Cyndee's resources for leaders include:

- *Rethinking Women's Ministry* Book and Workbook
- READ Bible Study Group Kit
- Prayer Warrior Boot Camp Online Course and Group Kit
- Bible Study Facilitator Training Online Course
- Women's Ministry Event Planning Online Course
- How to Select a Bible Study for Your Group Online Course
- *Women's Ministry Binder Essentials* eBook
- *Everything You Need to Know About Planning a Retreat* eBook
- *12 Days of Christmas Icebreaker Games* eBook

For more information, visit **womensministrytoolbox.com/resources.**

You can find her on Facebook, Instagram, and Pinterest @womensministrytoolbox and online at www.womensministrytoolbox.com.

Made in United States
North Haven, CT
04 October 2023

42323301R00117